CGP has the SATs reading test sorted!

Non-fiction reading questions can be tough, but this CGP SAT Buster
is packed with practice to help build pupils' skills and confidence!
It covers all eight reading elements from the KS2 English SATs:

- **2a** Word Meanings
- **2b** Fact Retrieval
- **2c** Summarising
- **2d** Inferences
- **2e** Predictions
- **2f** Structure
- **2g** Language
- **2h** Comparisons

There are separate question pages for each element, so it's simple
for pupils to spot what they're being asked to do. They'll learn how
to give exactly the right kind of answer in no time!

What's more, the fun Reading Raptor tick boxes ask pupils to assess how
they're doing, so you'll have an easy way to keep track of their progress.

Published by CGP

Editors: Izzy Bowen, Emma Crighton,
Catherine Heygate, Cathy Lear, Sean Walsh
Reviewer: Samantha Bensted

With thanks to Joe Brazier and Juliette Green
for the proofreading.
With thanks to Jan Greenway for the copyright
research.

ISBN: 978 1 78294 831 5

Clipart from Corel®
Printed by Elanders Ltd, Newcastle upon Tyne.

Based on the classic CGP style created by Richard Parsons.

Text, design, layout and original illustrations
© Coordination Group Publications Ltd. (CGP) 2017
All rights reserved.

Dare to Dance!

This piece of non-fiction is a leaflet about dancing. It explains why people like dancing and includes information about some different styles of dance. Perhaps it will convince you to give dancing a go.

What to do —

1) Open out the folding pages, and read the leaflet *Dare to Dance!*

2) Then read the text again. Look over each section closely to make sure you understand it.

3) Now take a break — chill out for a moment or two. Then warm yourself up again and have a go at the questions.

Turn the page.

Keep turning...

Dare to Dance!

When you hear music playing, do you long to get up and dance, but stick to clapping along because you think you have two left feet? Well, it's time to think again, because most basic dance steps are surprisingly easy to learn. What's more, with so many different dance styles out there, there's certain to be one that's right for you.

Why dance?

People learn to dance for many different reasons, but whether you're a complete beginner or a budding professional, dance classes can be very rewarding. For some, they're simply great fun. Others take dance lessons so that they can learn spectacular skills to show off to all their friends.

Another benefit of dancing — and one that people often overlook — is that it can be a great way to get fit. It gets the heart pumping and helps to build muscle. It can also help you improve your flexibility, meaning you'll be touching your toes in no time.

Which style of dance is right for me?

Before you choose a dance style, there are a few things to consider, including the sort of music you enjoy and whether you'd prefer to dance with a partner or individually. However, the most important thing is to start your dancing journey with an open mind — don't give up if the first style you try isn't the perfect fit.

Ballet

When you think of ballet, you might imagine pink leotards and tutus, but many ballet dancers train as hard as athletes. They perform impressive leaps and high-flying lifts, while making it all look completely effortless. Ballet can also really help you pick up other forms of dance, so it's a great place for beginners to start.

Hip-hop

Hip-hop dancing has become hugely popular, partly because it is often performed in music videos. Breakdancing is a form of hip-hop which often involves doing moves close to the ground, such as headspins (not to be tried at home!). 'Locking' is another form of hip-hop, where the dancer freezes in position between moves. Some hip-hop dancers are self-taught, but classes are also available.

Ballroom and Latin

Ballroom and Latin dancing were once seen as old-fashioned. However, thanks to celebrity dance competitions on television, classes for these dance types are now springing up all over the place. These types of dance involve performing a series of steps with a partner, some in hold and some apart. You might have heard of the waltz and the quickstep, or classic Latin styles like samba and salsa, but there are also many more styles to try.

Ali's story: Tap Dancing

"I always thought I was too clumsy to be a dancer, but then my best friend dragged me along to a tap class. Rhythm is really important for tap dancing, and because I play the drums I already had a good sense of rhythm. I enjoy making all the different sounds on the floor with my tap shoes — it feels a bit like playing the drums.

"I'm looking forward to giving my first performance soon, although I'm a bit nervous!"

Once you've found the dance style that's right for you, learning to dance is sure to be challenging, interesting and, above all, enjoyable. Your feet won't stop moving once you've caught the dancing bug!

2b   *Fact Retrieval Questions*

FACT RETRIEVAL questions ask you to find key bits of information from the text.
Have a look back at the text and then try answering these questions.

1. The introduction tells us that many basic dance steps are

tiring to learn	easy to learn	hard to learn	boring to learn

1 mark

Circle your answer.

2. Read the paragraph beginning **'People learn to dance for...'**

According to this paragraph, why do people learn to dance?

Give **two** reasons.

....

....

2 marks

3. Give **one** way dancing can help you get fit.

....

1 mark

4. Read the paragraph beginning **'Before you choose a dance style...'**

Give **one** thing you should consider before choosing a dance style.

....

....

1 mark

5. Why is ballet a particularly good dance style for beginners to learn?

....

....

1 mark

Fact Retrieval Questions

6. Which of these sentences is a reason why hip-hop is popular?

Tick **one** box.

You can wear baggy clothes. ☐

You can do it with your friends. ☐

It's the easiest dance style to learn. ☐

It's often performed in music videos. ☐

1 mark

7. Breakdancing often involves

| making sounds with your shoes | dancing without any music | doing moves near to the ground | dancing with a partner |

1 mark

Circle your answer.

8. Based on the text, give **two** types of Latin dancing.

....

....

2 marks

9. Who introduced Ali to tap dancing?

....

1 mark

10. Why is Ali feeling nervous?

....

1 mark

Reading Raptors can retrieve any fact easily. How did you get on with these questions? Give yourself a tick.

Section 1 — Dare to Dance!

2d

Inference Questions

INFERENCE questions are all about figuring things out from the text — you have to be a bit of a reading detective. See if you can snoop out the answers to these questions.

1. According to the introduction, why might the reader avoid dancing?

    ....

    ....

    | 1 mark |

2. Read the paragraph beginning **'Before you choose a dance style...'**

    Why might a beginner need to try more than one dance style?

    ....

    ....

    | 1 mark |

3. Read the paragraph beginning **'When you think of ballet...'**

    What evidence is there in this paragraph that ballet dancers are strong?

    ....

    ....

    | 2 marks |

4. Find and copy a phrase which suggests that breakdancing can be dangerous.

    ....

    | 1 mark |

5. **'...classes for these dance types are now springing up all over the place.'**

    What does this tell you about ballroom and Latin dancing today?

They are very unpopular.	They have become less popular.	Their popularity has not changed.	They are very popular.

    | 1 mark |

    Circle your answer.

2d ## *Inference Questions*

6. Put a tick in the correct box to show whether each statement is
   a fact or an opinion.

	Fact	Opinion
There are lots of different dance styles.		
Ballet dancers are impressive to watch.		
'Locking' involves freezing in position between moves.		
Ballroom and Latin dancing belong in the past.		

1 mark

7. Read the section called **'Ali's story: Tap Dancing'**.

   How can you tell that Ali was reluctant to go to the tap classes at first?

   ....

1 mark

8. Why was tap dancing a good choice of dance style for Ali? Give **two** reasons.

   ....

   ....

   ....

2 marks

9. **'Your feet won't stop moving once you've caught the dancing bug!'**

   What does this suggest about people who enjoy dancing?

   ....

   ....

1 mark

Making inferences is a Reading Raptor's favourite hobby. Tick to show how you got on with these pages.

2a

Word Meaning Questions

Some words are trickier than others — that's just the way it is. WORD MEANING questions check that you know the meanings of different words from the text. Have a go at these.

1. **'...so that they can learn spectacular skills to show off to all their friends.'**

   Circle the word that is closest in meaning to the word **'spectacular'**.

   | impressive | funny | dangerous | simple | **1 mark** |

2. **'Another benefit of dancing — and one people often overlook — is that it can be a great way to get fit.'**

   What does the word **'overlook'** mean in this sentence? Circle your answer.

   | stare at | understand | remember | forget about | **1 mark** |

3. **'Before you choose a dance style, there are a few things to consider...'**
   What does the word **'consider'** mean in this sentence? Tick **one** box.

   discuss ☐

   think about ☐

   write down ☐

   explain ☐

   1 mark

4. **'These types of dance involve performing a series of steps with a partner...'**

   Which word in this sentence could be replaced with the word 'sequence'?

   1 mark

   ....

Reading Raptors know word meanings like the back of their claws. How about you? Tick a box.

Summary Questions

To answer SUMMARY questions, you need to think about the overall ideas and messages in the text. Read 'Dare to Dance!' again, then dive in with these questions.

1. The section **'Why dance?'** is about

people's reasons for dancing	why dance is better than other sports	which dance style is most fun	being a professional dancer

1 mark

Circle your answer.

2. The main message of the whole text is that

ballet is the best style of dance	all styles of dance are difficult	all styles of dance are easy	everyone should try dancing

1 mark

Circle your answer.

Structure Questions

STRUCTURE questions ask you to think about how things are organised in the text. Take another, closer look at the text before attempting these questions.

1. Write the numbers 1 to 4 in the boxes to put these parts of the text in the right order. The first one has been done for you.

How to choose a dance style ☐   Why dancing is good for you 1

Someone's experience of dancing ☐   Different dance types ☐

1 mark

2. How does the final paragraph of the text link back to the first?

....

....

1 mark

Questions like these are light work for Reading Raptors. How heavy did you find them?

Drive-in to 1950s America

*This text is about drive-in cinemas. These are large open-air cinemas.
People park in front of a big movie screen and watch the film from their
cars. Drive-in cinemas were very popular in America in the 1950s, but
some people still like to go to them today. Maybe you can find one near you.*

What to do —

1) Open out the folding pages, and
   read the non-fiction text *Drive-in to
   1950s America*.

2) Then hold the pages to your nose and
   take a sharp sniff to breathe in the
   information. That probably won't work
   though, so read the text again anyway.

3) Now check out the questions...

 *Turn the page.*

Drive-in to 1950s America

America in the 1950s is often remembered for its colourful diners with black-and-white checked floors, or for the polka dot dresses and cool leather jackets that people wore.

Many features of 1950s culture now belong in the history books, but lots of people still experience a thrill at the thought of this highly glamorous period. As these fifties fans will tell you, there's no better way to relive the 1950s lifestyle than to take a trip to a drive-in cinema.

Movies in the Great Outdoors

The drive-in movie theatre — essentially a big outdoor cinema — has become an icon of life in 1950s America. People park in front of a large white screen and are then able to watch a film from the comfort of their own cars.

Drive-in cinemas revolutionised the movie-watching experience in the USA. At that time, the only other way for most people to see a film was to go to an indoor cinema, but these weren't always convenient. For example, the parents of young children needed a babysitter if they wanted to go to an evening screening at an indoor cinema. At a drive-in, parents could enjoy a film while their children slept in the back of the car. Drive-ins were also more convenient for pet owners, who could bring their furry friends along without fear of disturbing others.

The text continues over the page.

© CGP — not to be photocopied

Section 2 — Drive-in to 1950s America

The Origins of the Drive-in Cinema

Although there were a few outdoor cinemas in the early 1900s, the trend really got going in the 1930s. This was thanks to a man called Richard Milton Hollingshead Jr, who worked for his father's company selling car products. He noticed that people devoted a lot of time and money to their cars, and that they *really* liked going to the movies. Putting these

two things together, Hollingshead Jr had a brainwave — perhaps people would like to watch films from their cars. To test out this idea, he nailed a white screen between two trees, placed a radio behind it and attached a film projector to the front of his car. He also created a special ramp system so that the cars in each row were at different heights. This ensured that everyone had a clear view of the screen. In 1933, once he was sure the idea would work, Hollingshead Jr opened up the first proper drive-in cinema, with room for around 400 cars.

Sound Struggles

There were a few teething problems for the first drive-in cinemas. The film's sound had to be blasted out through massive speakers, which led to poor sound quality and to tension with people who lived nearby. Other techniques were tried, including speaker-posts located near each car, and speakers that hung on the cars' wing mirrors, but the solution only really emerged when built-in car radios became more common. People would tune in to a specific frequency, over which the film's audio was played, allowing them to hear it clearly and easily.

Movie Misery

Despite their popularity in the 1950s and 1960s, drive-in cinemas often struggled to make a profit. They could only screen films at night, which meant that the number of films they could show each day was very limited. They were also at the mercy of the weather, since rain and fog could put people off attending. Even worse, because they didn't make much money, they could only afford to show films that had already been screened at indoor cinemas. These older films just didn't draw in the crowds in the way the latest blockbusters did.

Drive-in cinemas were also hit hard by the march of technological progress. From the 1970s, it became ever easier for people to watch films at home. As a result, drive-ins were no longer the most convenient option for the movie-loving families and pet owners who had once found them so appealing.

Drive-in Cinemas Today

In the twenty-first century, drive-in cinemas continue to face an uphill battle. However, they are still treasured by those who want to experience a taste of the 'Golden Age' of Hollywood, a time between the 1930s and the 1960s when American movie-making was in its prime.

The majority of drive-in cinemas are found in the USA, but a few have begun to pop up around the UK, thanks to the popularity of American culture. Despite Britain's notoriously wet weather, a trip to a drive-in cinema can be an enjoyable and entertaining experience, offering movie-goers the opportunity to travel back in time and across the Atlantic without even stepping out of their cars.

Fact Retrieval Questions

FACT RETRIEVAL questions — they're all about noseying through the text to pick out the important information. Look back at the last three pages then answer these questions.

1. Read the first paragraph.

   Give **three** things that people often remember about America in the 1950s.

   ....

   ....

   ....

   3 marks

2. Why were indoor cinemas inconvenient for the parents of young children?

   ....

   ....

   1 mark

3. Why did Hollingshead Jr create a special ramp system for the cars?

   ....

   ....

   1 mark

4. When did Hollingshead Jr open the first proper drive-in cinema?

   | 1932 | 1933 | 1934 | 1935 |

   1 mark

   Circle your answer.

5. How many cars could attend Hollingshead Jr's first drive-in cinema?

   1 mark

   ....

Fact Retrieval Questions

6. **'The film's sound had to be blasted out through massive speakers...'**

Give **two** other techniques drive-in cinemas used to play the film's sound.

....

....

2 marks

7. At what time of day did drive-in cinemas show films?

afternoon	night	morning	lunchtime

1 mark

Circle your answer.

8. Why did drive-in cinemas find it difficult to make money? Tick **two** boxes.

They could only fit a few cars in front of the screen. ☐

They couldn't show many films each day. ☐

They were expensive. ☐

They were inconvenient. ☐

Bad weather put people off attending. ☐

1 mark

9. When was the 'Golden Age' of Hollywood?

1920s-1950s	1930s-1950s	1930s-1960s	1950s-1960s

1 mark

Circle your answer.

10. Where are most drive-in cinemas?

....

1 mark

Reading Raptors love a fact retrieval challenge.
Do you? Tick to show how these questions went.

Section 2 — Drive-in to 1950s America

2d # Inference Questions

INFERENCE questions are about reading between the lines. Well, not literally — don't start peering at your paper — but you do need to think about what bits of the text <u>really</u> mean.

1. The introduction suggests that many people think 1950s America was

exciting	surprising	confusing	strange

    1 mark

    Circle your answer.

2. '...there's no better way to relive the 1950s lifestyle than to take a trip to a drive-in cinema.'

    Is this a fact or an opinion?

    ....

    1 mark

3. Read the section called **'The Origins of the Drive-in Cinema'**.

    How can you tell that people's cars were important to them?

    ....

    1 mark

    ....

4. Read the paragraph beginning **'Drive-in cinemas were also...'**

    How did new technology affect drive-in cinemas? Explain your answer.

    ....

    ....

    2 marks

    ....

Inference Questions

2d

5. Read the section called **'Drive-in Cinemas Today'**.

    Find and copy a sentence which suggests that drive-in cinemas are still experiencing problems.

    ....

    ....

    1 mark

6. Read the paragraph beginning **'The majority of drive-in cinemas...'**

    Based on this paragraph, why might drive-in cinemas be less successful in Britain?

    Tick **one** box.

    People don't like films as much.   ☐

    The weather is often bad.   ☐

    There are more indoor cinemas.   ☐

    Fewer people have cars.   ☐

    1 mark

7. **'...travel back in time and across the Atlantic without even stepping out of their cars.'**

    How do you think this phrase makes the reader feel about going to a drive-in cinema? Give a reason for your answer.

    ....

    ....

    ....

    2 marks

Reading Raptors can answer inference questions standing on their heads. How about you?

Word Meaning Questions

To really understand a text, you need to have a good idea of what all the words are saying.
WORD MEANING questions ask you to think about the words used and their meanings.

1. '...could bring their furry friends along without fear of disturbing others.'

   What does the word **'disturbing'** mean in this sentence? Circle your answer.

   | embarrassing | amusing | threatening | distracting | 1 mark |

2. 'He noticed that people devoted a lot of time and money to their cars...'

   What does the word **'noticed'** mean in this sentence?

   ....   1 mark

3. '...the solution only really emerged when built-in car radios became more common.'

   Which word in this sentence could be replaced with the word 'answer'?

   ....   1 mark

4. '...for the movie-loving families and pet owners who had once found them so appealing.'

   Circle the word that means the same as **'appealing'** in this sentence.

   | attractive | off-putting | unusual | annoying | 1 mark |

Reading Raptors are brilliant at defining words.
How well did you manage to work out their meanings?

The last few questions on Drive-in to 1950s America are under here. ▶

Summary Questions

 2c

For these SUMMARY questions, read the whole text again, paying attention to the overall meaning of each section. Then try your hand at answering these questions.

1. Which phrase best summarises the two sections on page 14?

How drive-in cinemas developed	Benefits of drive-in cinemas	Hollingshead Jr's idea	Problems of drive-in cinemas

1 mark

   Circle your answer.

2. Read the section called **'Movie Misery'**.

   Which phrase would you use to summarise this section? Tick **one** box.

   Movies became unpopular. ☐

   Film technology improved. ☐

   Drive-in cinemas had money issues. ☐

   People went to drive-in cinemas more. ☐

1 mark

 2g

Language Question

LANGUAGE questions are designed to get you thinking about why a writer might have chosen the words and phrases they use. Have a go at this question to test your skills.

1. 'They were also at the mercy of the weather...'

   Why do you think the writer chose the phrase **'at the mercy of the weather'** to describe drive-in cinemas?

   ....

   ....

1 mark

Reading Raptors always get a rapturous applause for summary and language questions. How about you?

Inside the World of Jam

This text is a magazine article that gives you lots of information about jam. The writer of the article goes to meet some people who make and sell their own jam, as well as trying some out for himself.

What to do —

1) Read the non-fiction text *Inside the World of Jam* — you'll need to turn over for some of it.

2) Then read it again so that you know it inside-out, back-to-front and left-to-right.

3) Take your brain on a mini-adventure — swim through shark-infested waters and trek through a jungle to reach a secret cave... Then speed on to the questions.

SATURDAY 14th JULY — **FOOD WEEKLY**

Inside the World of Jam

Reporter and self-styled jam enthusiast Benjamin Dejar lifts the lid on this much-loved conserve.

I'll come right out and admit it: I'm a jam fanatic. I can't imagine a world in which my day doesn't begin with two slices of toast, topped with lashings of sweet, sticky jam. And while jam is mostly a breakfast food, I find it equally irreplaceable elsewhere. Without jam, a tea-time scone would be flavourless and disappointing, and I think we can all agree that a jam-free Victoria sponge would be an insult to cake lovers everywhere.

At breakfast-time I've often found myself pondering just how little I know about jam, despite the fact that I consume some every single day. So, armed with a pen and paper, I went to visit some of Britain's top jam-makers — fellow jam lovers who have taken their obsession one step further, dedicating themselves to making the very finest hand-made jams.

Scones are traditionally served with jam, as well as clotted cream or butter.

Traditional flavours

My first visit is to Robert Jacobs, founder of Jam On The Range. When the season is right and the fruit is ripe, Robert, a retired

The article continues over the page. ➡

farmer, retreats to the kitchen of his 18th-century Cheshire farmhouse, dons his apron and creates batches of hand-crafted jam. These spreads now have a small but devoted following in the UK, and Robert has recently ventured into international waters, with new customers in Germany and Switzerland.

His jams have received rave reviews from customers and critics alike, but Robert refuses to increase the number of jars he makes. As far as he's concerned, time, care and attention are the most important ingredients for a top-notch jar of jam. He remains nobly unwilling to compromise these values just for the sake of a larger profit.

In Robert's kitchen, the jam-making process is traditional: his recipes have been passed down through generations of the Jacobs family. He still uses almost identical techniques to his ancestors, although Robert admits he has "made a few tweaks" over the years in the name of perfecting the taste and texture.

When I ask him exactly what goes into his jam to make it so delicious, he chuckles heartily.

"If I told you, I'd have to tell everybody," he says. "And then where would we be?"

He does eventually give me one scrap of information. Apparently, the real secret to great jam lies in the fruit — freshly-picked, just ripe fruit from top-quality plants consistently produces better-tasting jam.

The morning after my visit, I try some of Robert's classic strawberry jam with my breakfast, and struggle to stop myself from gobbling up the rest of the jar by the spoonful.

New frontiers

Robert's flavours are traditional — he mostly produces strawberry, raspberry and blackcurrant, all of which are well-recognised flavours that appear regularly on the breakfast table.

But for Lara Fontesca, who owns and runs jam company Urban Jam, there are no limits to the flavour combinations that can go into a jam.

Urban Jam HQ is in the kitchen of Lara's Manchester home. She has transformed it into a full-time workspace where she can cook up her unusual jams, which range from the relatively run-of-the-mill (such as the bestselling apple and cinnamon flavour) to the outlandish.

"I'm working on a tomato ketchup flavour at the moment," explains Lara as we tour her bright, airy workspace. "If nothing else, it'll completely transform the way people look at the humble chip butty."

Lara Fontesca experiments with alternative flavours.

rewarding than using my imagination to transform the humble pot of jam."

The jams that she makes are nothing short of spectacular. I'll admit to grimacing in dismay when I heard that she wanted me to try her famous bacon sandwich flavour jam, but the explosion of flavour on my taste buds is more than enough to convince me of her expert skills as a jam-maker.

I end up with a large jar tucked into my bag for later, along with a few other flavours that caught my eye.

As I'm heading towards the door, I can't resist asking Lara one last question, from one jam enthusiast to another: what is the secret to a truly brilliant jam?

"Patience," she says without hesitating. "Patience and a working fire alarm."

And, with that knowledge under my belt, I head out of Urban Jam HQ, already making plans for tomorrow's breakfast.

Lara began crafting her own jams three years ago, when her children became bored with the spreads she purchased from her local supermarket.

"Setting up the business has been a huge challenge," she tells me, "but I've never been tempted to give up. For me, there's nothing more

 Open the flap for the start of the text.

Unfold these pages before you start

2b

Fact Retrieval Questions

Grab your compass and your map — it's time for a FACT RETRIEVAL journey.
These questions will help you practise those all-important fact-finding skills.

1. What is Benjamin Dejar's job?

| stylist | farmer | reporter | jam-maker |

1 mark

Circle your answer.

2. a) For his breakfast, what does Benjamin Dejar eat with jam?

....

1 mark

b) Benjamin Dejar mentions **two** more foods for which jam is essential.
   What are they?

....

....

2 marks

3. Write down **two** countries where Robert sells his jams.

....

....

2 marks

4. Put a tick in the correct box to show whether each statement is true or false.

	True	False
Robert Jacobs makes jam all year round.		
Robert makes his jam at home.		
Robert uses old family recipes to make his jam.		
Robert has never changed the recipes he uses.		

1 mark

2b

Fact Retrieval Questions

5. Which Jam On The Range flavour does Benjamin Dejar try?

| blackcurrant | strawberry | apple | raspberry | **1 mark** |

Circle your answer.

6. Lara Fontesca is in the middle of creating a new flavour of jam.
What flavour is it?

| tomato ketchup | apple and cinnamon | chip butty | bacon sandwich | **1 mark** |

Circle your answer.

7. For how many years has Lara Fontesca been making jam?

.... **1 mark**

8. Why did Lara Fontesca decide to make her own jam?

....

.... **1 mark**

9. What **two** things does Lara Fontesca say are needed to make good jam?

....

.... **2 marks**

Reading Raptors can find facts in the deepest, darkest depths. How did you get on?

2d *Inference Questions*

If you're a detective at heart, INFERENCE questions will be just your cup of tea — they're all about finding clues in the text, and using them to work out things that aren't too obvious.

1. Why does Benjamin Dejar decide to visit some of Britain's top jam-makers?

    ....   **1 mark**

2. Read the paragraph on page 24 that begins **'His jams have received...'**

    How can you tell that Robert Jacobs cares about the quality of his jam?

    ....

    ....   **1 mark**

3. What evidence is there that Robert Jacobs is secretive about how his jams are made?

    ....

    ....   **1 mark**

4. How can you tell that Benjamin Dejar enjoys eating Robert Jacobs's jam?

    ....

    ....   **1 mark**

5. Read the paragraph beginning **'Robert's flavours are traditional...'**

    How can you tell from this paragraph that the flavours Robert uses are popular?

    ....

    ....   **1 mark**

2d *Inference Questions*

6. Put a tick in the correct box to show whether each statement is a fact or an opinion.

	Fact	Opinion
Lara Fontesca lives in Manchester.		
Lara makes more than one flavour of jam.		
Lara's tastiest jam is apple and cinnamon flavour.		
Supermarket jam flavours are boring.		

1 mark

7. Look at the part of the text that starts **"'I'm working on...'** and ends **'...the humble pot of jam.'"**

What impressions do you get of Lara Fontesca from these paragraphs?

Support your answer with evidence from the text.

....

....

....

3 marks

8. How can you tell that Benjamin Dejar did not want to try the bacon sandwich flavour jam?

....

1 mark

9. How do you think Benjamin Dejar feels about Lara Fontesca's jams?

Use evidence from the text to support your answer.

....

....

2 marks

Reading Raptors can always work out what the writer's on about. How did you get on with these questions?

© CGP — not to be photocopied

Section 3 — Inside the World of Jam

Word Meaning Questions

WORD MEANING questions really get you thinking about the meaning of specific words and phrases in the text. Have a go at flexing your vocabulary muscles with these questions.

1. **'...I've often found myself pondering just how little I know about jam...'**

   What does the word **'pondering'** mean in this sentence?

   ....

   1 mark

2. Look at the paragraph beginning **'I'm working on...'**

   Find and copy **one** word which could be replaced with the word 'change'.

   ....

   1 mark

3. **'There's nothing more rewarding than using my imagination...'**

   What does the word **'rewarding'** mean in this sentence?

   ....

   1 mark

4. **'"Patience," she says without hesitating.'**

   What does the word **'hesitating'** mean in this sentence?

   Tick **one** box.

   listening ☐

   hearing ☐

   pausing ☐

   moving ☐

   1 mark

Reading Raptors can swallow word meaning questions whole. How did you find them?

The last few questions on *Inside the World of Jam* are under here. ➤

Summary Questions

SUMMARY questions are about being able to understand larger chunks of the text, or even the whole thing. Have a bash at these questions to test your summarising skills.

1. How can the section **'Traditional flavours'** be summarised?

It tells you how to sell jam for large profits.	It tells you about two different jam companies.	It tells you strawberry is the best jam flavour.	It tells you about a jam company in Cheshire.	**1 mark**

   Circle your answer.

2. Which of these sentences is a main idea of the section called **'New frontiers'**?

Tick **one** box.

Not all flavours of jam taste nice. ☐

Everyone should learn to make jam. ☐

It's possible to experiment with jam flavours. ☐

Imagination can solve any problem. ☐

1 mark

Comparison Question

COMPARISON questions are about things that are similar or different in the text. Look at each section of the article closely to be sure you understand it, then try this question.

1. How are Robert Jacobs's jams different to Lara Fontesca's jams?

   Use evidence from the text to support your answer.

   ....

   ....

   ....

   2 marks

Reading Raptors do summary questions for lunch and comparison questions for pudding. How about you?

The Great Wall of China

This text is about the Great Wall of China. It contains information about what the wall looks like, who built it and the threats that it faces. It also describes some myths about the wall, and what the real facts are.

What to do —

1) Read the non-fiction text *The Great Wall of China* — you'll need to turn over for some of it.

2) Now have another read. That way you'll be sure you've understood it all.

3) Then take a mini break — imagine riding the world's fastest rollercoaster. Now that's got your heart pumping, turn over and try the questions.

The Great Wall of China

Snaking its way across northern China, the Great Wall of China is one of the world's most recognisable sights. Stretching into the distance as far as the human eye can see, the extensive grey and brown barrier cuts through several Chinese provinces and a range of landscapes, including lush green countryside, arid desert and steep mountain passes. Its many fortresses and towers break up the seemingly endless path of stone and bring memories of China's distant past to life. Visitors to these fortresses and towers walk in the footsteps of the soldiers who were once stationed along the wall, keeping a wary eye out for attackers and using beacons to send messages along the line.

The wall's name in Chinese literally translates to 'long wall', and no other man-made structure reaches further. A widespread myth about the Great Wall is that it is visible from the moon. However, astronauts attest that even this enormous feat of human engineering cannot be seen with the naked eye at such a distance, and the wall's similarity in shape to other natural landmarks like rivers makes it hard to recognise even from a point much closer to the Earth. The only way to spot the wall from space would be to use a powerful telescope or camera.

Another popular misconception about the wall is that it is a single continuous structure. Instead, it's actually a set of several different walls, some running parallel to one another or meeting at junctions. The official length of the wall, including all these different parts, is estimated at over 13,000 miles.

The article continues over the page.

The Great Wall has such a piecemeal structure because it was constructed by several different rulers over more than 2000 years. The wall first began to take its modern-day shape when the first Emperor of China joined together several smaller, existing walls to protect the country against invasion from the north. The wall was then extended during the Han dynasty* (206 BC – 220 AD) as a way to safeguard the Silk Road, a trade route along which luxury foods, precious stones, and fabrics such as silk were transported.

The final section of the wall was built over a millennium later, during the Ming dynasty (1368-1644). As before, this section combined new stretches of wall and older, existing sections, which were repaired or rebuilt. This section, which is known as the 'Ming Great Wall', is measured at over 5,500 miles, although some of this length is made up of mountains, lakes and rivers that formed a 'natural wall' against invaders. Most of the wall that is now visible was built during this period, so it is the Ming Great Wall that is most frequently visited by tourists today.

The immense scale of the Great Wall proves the ambition and determination of the societies involved in building it. Parts of the wall were formed from bricks or slabs of stone, which were cut into shape and then loaded into place. The workforce consisted of soldiers as well as poor farmers and criminals who had been forced into labour. Materials were painstakingly borne up to the wall on the backs and shoulders of the labourers, or in bamboo baskets. It was dangerous and exhausting work, which claimed the lives of many of the labourers; some were even buried within the wall itself.

A famous legend tells the story of Meng Jiangnu, whose husband was killed while working on the wall and entombed within its stones. According to the rumour, her tears prompted the bricks around his body to disintegrate, enabling her to retrieve his remains and give them a proper burial.

* dynasty — a series of rulers from the same family

In the centuries after the fall of the Ming dynasty, the wall was largely abandoned. It was only in the middle of the twentieth century that the Chinese government began a mission to protect and rebuild it. In December 1987, the wall was named a UNESCO World Heritage Site — a place that is considered especially important and valuable to humankind. As a World Heritage Site, the wall is protected under international law, and efforts to conserve it for future generations are encouraged.

Today, some sections of the Great Wall have been fully restored and made easily accessible to visitors. For example, cable cars have been erected at several points, allowing visitors to avoid a steep climb up hundreds of steps. Thanks in part to this, the wall is now a leading tourist attraction in China — in the busy summer season, just one section can receive up to 70,000 visitors in a single day.

However, while most visitors treat the wall with the respect it deserves, some spoil its historic beauty by leaving litter or drawing graffiti. Shocking damage has been caused by human actions — some parts have even been destroyed to make way for roads. The wall also faces other threats that are putting it in danger. Being extremely old, it has suffered a great deal from the effects of erosion, which have caused whole chunks to crumble away. As a result, some parts of the wall, especially the north-western sections, are believed to require urgent restoration if they are still to be standing in twenty years' time.

Despite the dilapidated state of some sections, the Great Wall is still one of the most astonishing human structures on the planet today, and a record of many centuries of Chinese history.

← *Open the flap for the start of the text.*

Section 4 — The Great Wall of China

Unfold these pages before you start

2b *Fact Retrieval Questions*

For FACT RETRIEVAL questions, you need to burrow through the text like a mole. Use your searching skills to uncover the answers to these questions.

1.   Give **one** type of landscape the Great Wall goes through.

....

1 mark

2.   What would you need in order to be able to see the Great Wall from space?

....

1 mark

3.   How long is the Great Wall?

less than 5,500 miles	less than 10,000 miles	more than 13,000 miles	more than 70,000 miles

1 mark

Circle your answer.

4.   Read the paragraph beginning **'The Great Wall has such a piecemeal structure...'**

Why was the Great Wall built? Give **two** reasons.

....

....

....

2 marks

5.   Name **one** thing that was transported along the Silk Road.

....

1 mark

Fact Retrieval Questions

6. When did the Great Wall become a UNESCO World Heritage Site?

....

1 mark

7. According to the text, how has the Great Wall been made more accessible for visitors?

| Cable cars have been put up. | Entry fees have been reduced. | A cafe has been built on the wall. | There are longer opening times. |

1 mark

Circle your answer.

8. Which of the following facts can be found in this text? Tick **two** boxes.

The Great Wall is found in southern China. ☐

There are many towers along the Great Wall. ☐

The Great Wall was built by just one ruler. ☐

Soldiers helped to build the Great Wall. ☐

The Great Wall has been fully restored. ☐

1 mark

9. Read the paragraph beginning '**However, while most visitors...**'

How has the Great Wall been damaged over time? Give **three** ways.

....

....

....

3 marks

Reading Raptors can race through fact retrieval questions. Can you? Tick to show how you got on.

© CGP — not to be photocopied

Section 4 — The Great Wall of China

Inference Questions

To answer INFERENCE questions, you need to read the sentences in the text and work out what they're really saying. Take a look back at the text and then have a go at these questions.

1. Find and copy a phrase from the first paragraph which suggests that many people know what the Great Wall looks like.

   ....

   1 mark

2. When the writer says **'the extensive grey and brown barrier cuts through several Chinese provinces'**, are they stating a fact or giving an opinion?

   ....

   1 mark

3. Read the first paragraph. How might visiting a fortress or tower help **'bring memories of China's distant past to life'**?

Visitors can try using a beacon.	**Visitors can walk where soldiers did.**	**Visitors can meet a real soldier.**	**Visitors can read soldiers' messages.**

   1 mark

   Circle your answer.

4. Look at the paragraph beginning **'The wall's name in Chinese...'**

   Find and copy a phrase that suggests that many people believe the wall is visible from the moon.

   ....

   1 mark

5. Why would mountains, lakes and rivers be a **'natural wall'** against invaders?

   ....

   ....

   2 marks

2d | *Inference Questions*

6. Look at the paragraph beginning **'The immense scale of the Great Wall...'**

What evidence is there that building the Great Wall was hard work?

....

....

....

| 2 marks |

7. How do you know that the story of Meng Jiangnu may not be true?

| 1 mark |

....

8. Why do you think the Great Wall is considered **'especially important and valuable to humankind'**? Explain your answer with reference to the text.

....

....

....

....

| 3 marks |

9. Read the paragraph beginning **'However, while most visitors...'**

How do you think the writer feels about people causing damage to the Great Wall? Use evidence from the text to support your answer.

....

....

....

| 2 marks |

Reading Raptors can do inference questions faster than you can say 'Raptors rule'. How about you?

Word Meaning Questions

To do WORD MEANING questions, you need to know what the words the writer has used mean. Have another read of the text to refresh your memory, then try these questions.

1. **'...keeping a wary eye out for attackers...'**

   What does the word **'wary'** mean in this sentence?

   Tick **one** box.

   confident ☐

   cautious ☐

   bored ☐

   sleepy ☐

   1 mark

2. Read from **'The final section...'** to **'...within the wall itself.'**

   Find and copy a word from this section which means 'huge'.

   ....

   1 mark

3. **'...her tears prompted the bricks around his body to disintegrate...'**

   Which word from this sentence tells you that the bricks broke into pieces?

   ....

   1 mark

4. Look at page 35.

   Find and copy **one** word from this page which tells you that the Great Wall is one of China's most popular tourist destinations.

   ....

   1 mark

Reading Raptors know the meanings of even the trickiest words. Do you? Give yourself a tick.

Section 4 — The Great Wall of China